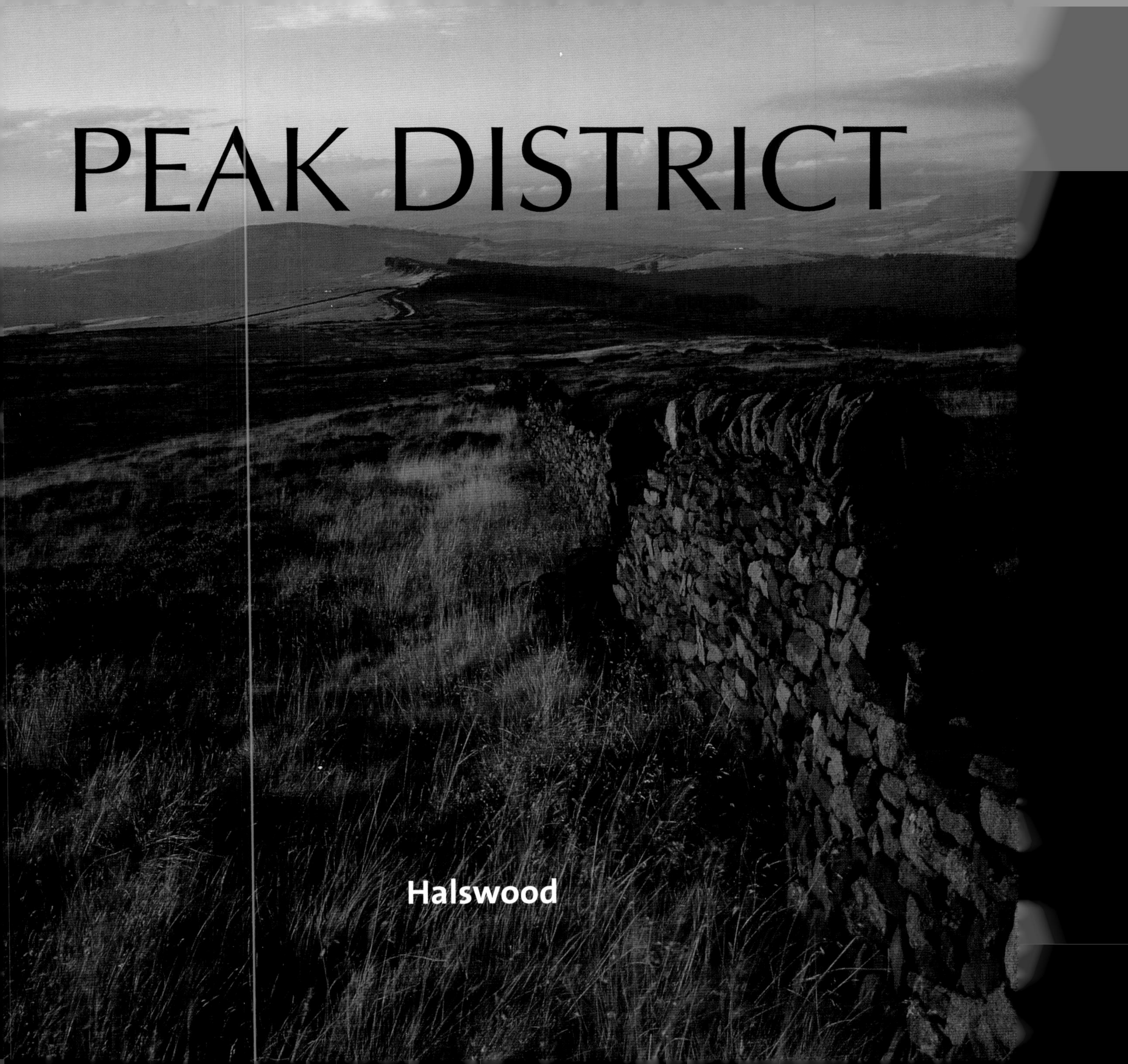

PEAK DISTRICT

Halswood

Published by Halswood Stationers

British Library Cataloguing-in-Publication Data
A CIP record for this title is available from the British Library

ISBN 978 0 85717 006 4

HALSWOOD STATIONERS
Halsgrove House,
Ryelands Industrial Estate,
Bagley Road, Wellington, Somerset TA21 9PZ
Tel: 01823 653777 Fax: 01823 216796
email: sales@halsgrove.com

Part of the Halsgrove group of companies
Information on all Halsgrove titles is available at:
www.halsgrove.com

Printed and bound in China by
Toppan Leefung Printing Ltd (0)

Front cover: Fluffy white heads of cotton grass add lightness and movement to this moorland view across Gradbach to Three Shire Heads.

Back cover: Three Shire Heads. An icy River Dane flows under the old packhorse bridge where the three counties of Staffordshire, Cheshire and Derbyshire meet.

Title page: A late evening view north from Pym Chair.

Overleaf: Storm over Crowdecote.

The undulating crest of Chrome Hill, known locally as the Dragon's Back, rises above the early morning mist in the Upper Dove Valley.

INTRODUCTION

The 555 square miles (1438 square km) of the Peak District National Park, the first in the country to be so designated way back in 1951, lie at the southern end of the Pennines and form a marked transition between the soft green lowlands and the harsh moorland uplands. Surrounded by the conurbations of Manchester, Sheffield and the Midlands, it's not surprising that the park is the most popular in the UK.

The Peak landscape consists of two clearly defined types of scenery produced by different rocks. The high, bleak gritstone moorland forms a horseshoe known as the Dark Peak, and enclosed within this inverted "U" is the rolling limestone area of the White Peak, an undulating plateau of high pastureland split by dramatic dales.

In this varied landscape each season has its own beauty. This ranges from the colourful display of wild flowers during springtime; the purple-clad heather moors in high summer; the golden autumnal colours of the trees below the eastern edges; to the Arctic-like snowy wastes of the high lands in winter.

Chasing the light across this precious landscape can be very rewarding but also requires great patience – sitting on the top of a hill waiting for the sun to rise only to find a bank of cloud rolling in from the east blocking out the magical dawn light, or sheltering behind rocks waiting for heavy rain to pass over and leave dramatic clouds, sunbeams and rainbows. In rapidly changing light, pictures can appear and disappear in seconds.

You will find some pictures in this book with azure skies and bright sunshine, but the photographer, the masterly Jerry Rawson, prefers the impact of dramatic light, stormy conditions and especially around dawn and dusk when the light can be a revelation transforming the mundane landscape into something quite sublime; capturing a fleeting moment of perfection.

Address books tend to be well used and have a long life. Along with important contact details, they keep track of the user's friends and acquaintances, tracing their lives over time and from place to place. And, if properly attended to, an address book eventually becomes a journal in itself, and an attractive and permanent keepsake. Whether bought as a gift or for personal use, this *Peak District Address Book*, with its superb pictorial reminders of the national park, will provide years of pleasure.

USEFUL ADDRESSES AND TELEPHONE NUMBERS

A

Five Wells Tomb. The rays of the setting sun illuminate the Five Wells Neolithic chambered tomb – one of the highest chambered tombs in England – overlooking the Wye Valley near Taddington.

A

Spring sunshine warms a stone barn on the edge of the village of Chelmorton.

Early morning mist rises from the Wye as it weaves its way through Chee Dale.

B

B

B

The beautiful wooded valley of Water-cum-Jolly Dale, through which the River Wye flows on its journey south.

D

A snowy view across Gradbach to the shapely peak of Shutlingsloe, its flanks criss-crossed by gritstone walls.

D

D

D

A lone rowan tree with its red berries set among heather moorland acts as a foreground for this view north over Goldsitch Moss to the dome of Axe Edge.

Evening sunshine highlights the series of eroded boulders and dramatic pinnacles at Ramshaw Rocks, near Leek.

E

E

E

Mermaid's Pool. A winter sunset reflected in Blake
Mere, which retains the legend of a mermaid.

Fluffy white heads of cotton grass add lightness and movement to this moorland view across Gradbach to Three Shire Heads.

F

F

F

A storm approaches the upper reaches of the Goyt Valley on the moors west of Buxton.

Clusters of bilberry dominate this view along the craggy skyline of Kinder Scout's northern edges.

H

H

H

A spectrum of colours contrasts with the dark, brooding storm clouds over Bleaklow.

A vibrant mix of autumn colours add charm to this view across Ladybower Reservoir to the tor-topped Derwent Edge.

Nestling below the escarpment of Stanage Edge, Overstones Farm forms a lovely foreground for this view up the Derwent Valley to Win Hill and the distant Kinder Scout.

J

The gritstone buttresses of Stanage Edge overlook golden bracken slopes lit by the rays of the setting sun.

J

A vibrant mix of greens and golds below the rearing gritstone buttresses of the Roaches.

K

Abandoned stacks of millstones or grindstones below Stanage Edge. Hewn from gritstone using simple hand tools, the production of these stones was once an important Peak District industry.

K

A winter sunset across the Derwent Valley, captured from Higger Tor.

L

A tapestry of colour of ancient beech trees in
Yarncliffe Wood, Upper Padley Gorge.

L

L

L

Looking south-east along Curbar Edge to Baslow Edge and Chatsworth, as storm clouds drift across the landscape.

M

Evening light on gritstone boulders above Curbar Edge, with the moors of Kinder Scout and Bleaklow visible on the distant horizon.

M

M

M

Warm evening light brings out the rich autumn colours of the wooded slopes of the Derwent Valley, overlooking the village of Curbar.

N

The four remaining monoliths of the original nine dating back to the early Bronze Age which formed a stone circle on Harthill Moor.

N

Looking out across the wooded Bretton Clough from the outcrop of Gotheredge.

O

Three Shire Heads. An icy River Dane flows under the old packhorse bridge where the three counties of Staffordshire, Cheshire and Derbyshire meet.

O

The patchwork walled fields of Abney Low backed by the moors of the Dark Peak are seen in this view north from the moors near the summit of Sir William Hill road.

PQ

No walkers to be seen on an icy Peakland day.

PQ

A summer storm breaks over the White Peak plateau near Monyash at the northern end of Lathkill Dale.

S

Mam Tor, site of an Iron Age hillfort and now owned by the National Trust, dominates the head of the Hope Valley. The crumbling nature of Mam Tor's east face gives rise to the name 'Shivering Mountain.'

S

S

S

The last snows of winter on the skyline above Crowden Clough,
one of the finest approaches to the Kinder Scout plateau.

T

A frost-covered wall acts as a foreground for this dawn view west to Shutlingsloe, from near the Cat and Fiddle Inn on the Buxton to Macclesfield road.

T

A stream tumbles through a wooded glade below
Linch Clough in the Upper Derwent Valley.

The bare bones of the Bleaklow landscape.

UV

Dawn light paints the rocks on The Nab,
in this view across Grindsbrook to
Grindslow Knoll, Kinder Scout.

W

Dressed in an icy mantle, the craggy Back Tor lies on the ridge linking Mam Tor and Lose Hill.

W

Looking north to Dudwood Farm, with the gritstone pinnacles of Robin Hood's Stride on the wooded skyline on the edge of Harthill Moor, to the west of Birchover.

Grasses add a touch of colour to this bleak moorland landscape leading to Higher Shelf Stones and Bleaklow, seen from the Snake Pass.

XYZ